21ST CENTURY R
PIANO

CW00542244

PUBLISHED BY
WISE PUBLICATIONS
8/9 FRITH STREET, LONDON, W1D 3JB, ENGLAND.

EXCLUSIVE DISTRIBUTORS:
MUSIC SALES LIMITED
DISTRIBUTION CENTRE, NEWMARKET ROAD,
BURY ST EDMUNDS, SUFFOLK, IP33 3YB,
ENGLAND.
MUSIC SALES PTY LIMITED
120 ROTHSCHILD AVENUE, ROSEBERY,
NSW 2018, AUSTRALIA.

ORDER NO. AM90072
ISBN 0-7119-3136-4
THIS BOOK © COPYRIGHT 2004
BY WISE PUBLICATIONS.

COMPILED BY NICK CRISPIN.
MUSIC EDITED BY LUCY HOLLIDAY.
MUSIC ARRANGEMENTS BY DEREK JONES & PAUL HONEY.
MUSIC PROCESSED BY PAUL EWERS MUSIC DESIGN.

COVER DESIGN BY FRESH LEMON.
PRINTED IN THE UNITED KINGDOM BY
CALIGRAVING LIMITED, THETFORD, NORFOLK.

YOUR GUARANTEE OF QUALITY:
AS PUBLISHERS, WE STRIVE TO PRODUCE EVERY
BOOK TO THE HIGHEST COMMERCIAL STANDARDS.
THE MUSIC HAS BEEN FRESHLY ENGRAVED AND
THE BOOK HAS BEEN CAREFULLY DESIGNED
TO MINIMISE AWKWARD PAGE TURNS AND TO
MAKE PLAYING FROM IT A REAL PLEASURE.
PARTICULAR CARE HAS BEEN GIVEN TO
SPECIFYING ACID-FREE, NEUTRAL-SIZED
PAPER MADE FROM PULPS WHICH HAVE
NOT BEEN ELEMENTAL CHLORINE BLEACHED.
THIS PULP IS FROM FARMED SUSTAINABLE
FORESTS AND WAS PRODUCED WITH
SPECIAL REGARD FOR THE ENVIRONMENT.
THROUGHOUT, THE PRINTING AND BINDING HAVE
BEEN PLANNED TO ENSURE A STURDY,
ATTRACTIVE PUBLICATION WHICH
SHOULD GIVE YEARS OF ENJOYMENT.
IF YOUR COPY FAILS TO MEET OUR HIGH STANDARDS,
PLEASE INFORM US AND WE WILL GLADLY REPLACE IT.

WWW.MUSICSALES.COM

WISE PUBLICATIONS
LONDON / NEW YORK / PARIS / SYDNEY / COPENHAGEN / BERLIN / MADRID / TOKYO

AVALANCHE

WORDS & MUSIC BY RYAN ADAMS

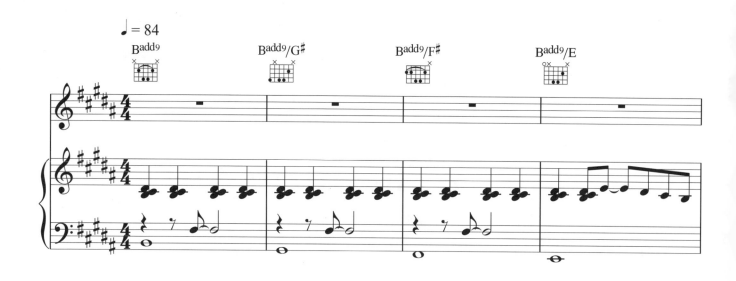

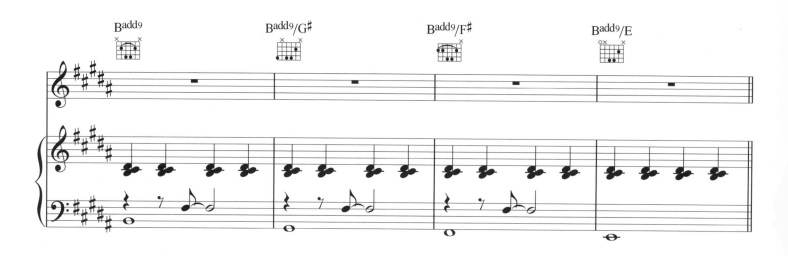

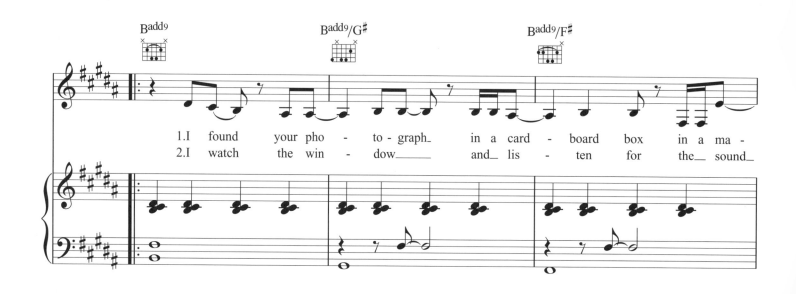

1. I found your pho-to-graph_ in a card-board box in a ma-
2. I watch the win-dow_____ and_ lis-ten for the_ sound_

4

CALIFORNIA
WORDS & MUSIC BY ALEX GREENWALD & JASON SCHWARTZMAN

1. We've been on the run, driv-ing in the sun, look-ing out for num-ber one,___ Ca - li - for-
2. On the ste - re - o, lis - ten as we go, no-thing's gon-na stop me now,___ Ca - li - for-

CENTREFOLDS

WORDS & MUSIC BY BRIAN MOLKO, STEFAN OLSDAL & STEVE HEWITT

Come on Bal - tha - za___   I re - fuse___ to let___ you die.___

___   Come on fall - ing star,___

DO NO WRONG

WORDS BY WILL SOUTH
MUSIC BY WILL SOUTH, TOM WELHAM, ADAM WILSON & BRENDON JAMES

1.Sa - tel - lites___ con - tain___ us,   traf - fic   lights___ con - trol___
(2.)Sum - mer sun___ pro - tects___ us,   win - ter   rains_____ tor -

18

Everybody's Changing

WORDS & MUSIC BY TIM RICE-OXLEY, TOM CHAPLIN & RICHARD HUGHES

1. You say___ you wan-

FLOWERS IN THE WINDOW

WORDS & MUSIC BY FRAN HEALY

1. When I ___ first held ___ you I ___ was cold, ___
(Verses 2 & 3 see block lyrics)

Oh,_ oh._____

Oh. _____

rit.

Let's watch the flow - ers_____ grow.

Verse 2:
There is no reason to feel bad
But there are many seasons to feel glad, sad, mad
It's just a bunch of feelings that we have to hold
But I am here to help you with the load.

Wow, look at you now *etc.*

Verse 3:
So now were here and now is fine
So far away from there and there is time, time, time
To plant new seeds and watch them grow
So there'll be flowers in the window when we go.

Wow, look at us now *etc.*

FOR LOVERS

WORDS & MUSIC BY PETER WOLFE, PETE DOHERTY, JULIAN TAYLOR,
MATT WHITE, NED SCOTT, MAFF SCOTT, DAVID BANKS & JAKE FIOR

1.I'm run-ning a-way__ with you, that's all I____ ev - er do.__
2.I'm run-ning a-way__ with you from____ yes - ter-day's news.__

And that's all we ev - er mean,__ but I for-give_ you ev-'ry-thing.__
Let's leave it all__ be-hind,__ help me back__ to my mind.__

GODDESS ON A HIWAY

WORDS & MUSIC BY JONATHAN DONAHUE, GRASSHOPPER, ADAM SNYDER & DAVID FRIDMANN

know   it ain't gon-na last.___   And I know   it ain't gon-na last.__

___   When I   see your eyes__ ar-rive__ they ex-plode   like two bugs   on

glass.__

HOMESICK
WORDS & MUSIC BY CRAIG NICHOLLS

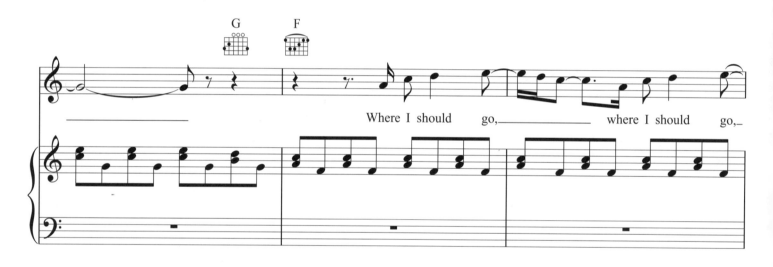

No-thing's gon-na save_ you, no-thing's gon-na save_ you out there.___

No-thing's gon-na save_ you, no-thing's gon-na save_ you out there.

rall.

HURT

WORDS & MUSIC BY TRENT REZNOR

1. I hurt my - self to - day to see if I still feel. I fo - cused on the pain, the on - ly thing that's

2. I wear this crown of thorns up - on my li - ars chair. Full of bro - ken thoughts, I can - not re -

goes a - way____ in the end.____ And
you could have____ it all,____ my em - pire of dirt.
I will let____ you down,____
I will make____ you hurt.____

LOOK WHAT YOU'VE DONE

WORDS & MUSIC BY NIC CESTER

1.Take my pho-to off the wall ___ if it just ___ won't sing for you. ___ 'Cause all that's left has gone a-way ___ and there's no-thing there ___ for you to prove. ___

for you.___ I can hard-ly hear you say___ ___ what should_ I do,_____ well_ you choose._____ Oh look what you've done___ you've made_ a fool_ of_ ev-'ry-one,_ oh well it seems like such fun___ un-til___ you lose_

IN OTHER WORDS

WORDS & MUSIC BY BEN KWELLER

1. A - no - ther night slips a - way, in oth - er words I should say there
(2.) mul - ti life is bet - ter than the one we're in, the one we knew, 'cause

are no words he should say. There are no words.
ev - 'ry - one is see - ing through, ev - 'ry - one.

In his eyes I see the fear that
Step - ping on his gold ter - rain, he's mov-

It starts stop - ping when it stops stop - ping. It starts stop - ping when it stops stop - ping.

It starts stop - ping when it stops stop - ping. It starts stop - ping when

it stops stop - ping. It starts stop - ping when it stops stop - ping.

It starts stop - ping yeah.___ Yeah, yeah, yeah, yeah, yeah, yeah.___

Repeat ad lib.

THE OTHER SIDE

WORDS & MUSIC BY DAVID GRAY

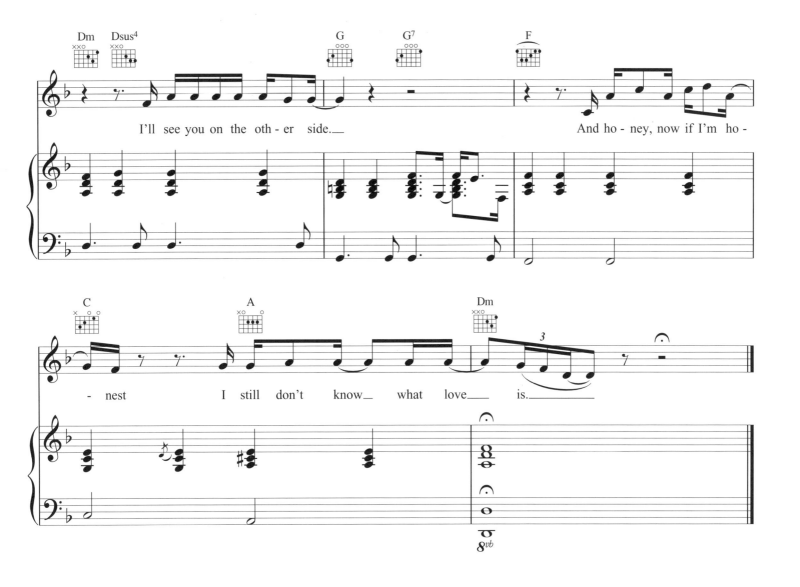

Verse 2:

Maybe I oughta mention
Was never my intention
To harm you or your kin
Are you so scared to look within
The ghosts are crawling on our skin
We may race and we may run
We'll not undo what has been done.

Verse 3:

I know it would be outrageous
To come on all courageous
And offer you my hand
To pull you up onto dry land
When all I got is sinking sand
That trick ain't worth the time it buys
I'm sick of hearing my own lies.

Queen of the Underworld

Words & Music by Jesse Malin

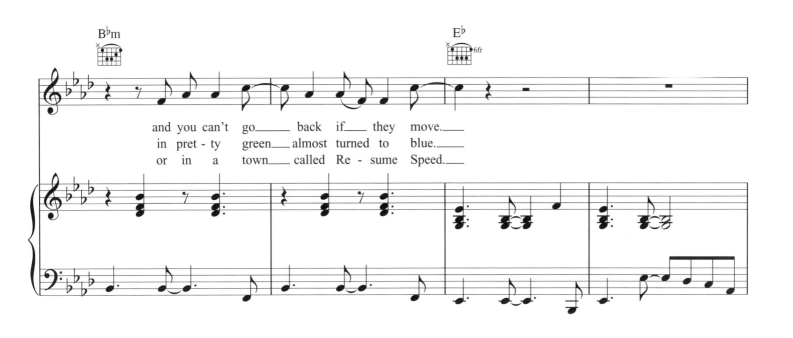

and you can't go____ back if____ they move.____
in pret - ty green____ almost turned to blue.____
or in a town____ called Re - sume Speed.____

From dis - func - tion to____ dis - func - tion,
Ev - 'ry - thing____ you've heard____ I've got - ten.
Out on the high - way of____ per - fec - tion.

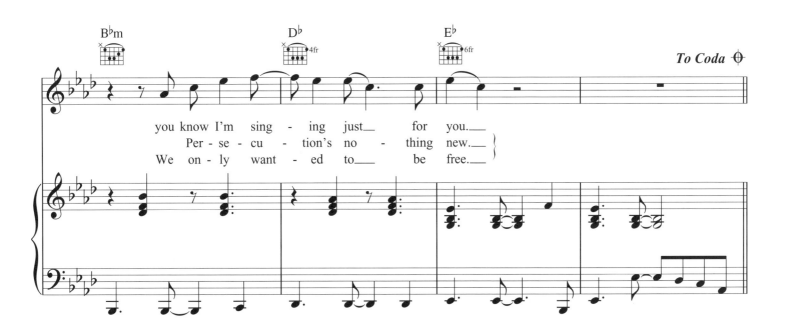

To Coda

you know I'm sing - ing just____ for you.____
Per - se - cu - tion's no - thing new.____
We on - ly want - ed to____ be free.____

3.I ne-ver got an in-vi-ta - tion, ne-ver heard too much.___

I'm gon-na make a re-ser-va - tion but I'm not in a rush.___

D.S. al Coda

Coda

Queen of the Un-der-world took a ride on the

SANTA CRUZ (YOU'RE NOT THAT FAR)

WORDS BY CONOR DEASY

MUSIC BY CONOR DEASY, KEVIN HORAN, PADRAIC McMAHON, DANIEL RYAN & BEN CARRIGAN

I heard a drink was in - volved._____
your train's just rolled in on time._____

Oh, you got - ta be,___ oh, you got - ta be___ still liv-

- ing by___ the sea.___ Oh, you got - ta be,___ oh, you got -

- ta be,___ 'cause San - ta Cruz___ you're not___ that

72

Santa Cruz,___ no, you're not that far.___ 2. But

Banjo

THE SCIENTIST

WORDS & MUSIC BY GUY BERRYMAN, JON BUCKLAND, WILL CHAMPION & CHRIS MARTIN

1. Come up to meet you, tell you I'm sorry, you don't know how love-
2. I was just guessing at numbers and figures, pulling the puz-

-ly you are._____ I had to find____ you, tell you I need__

-zles a - part._____ Ques - tions of sci - ence, sci - ence and pro -

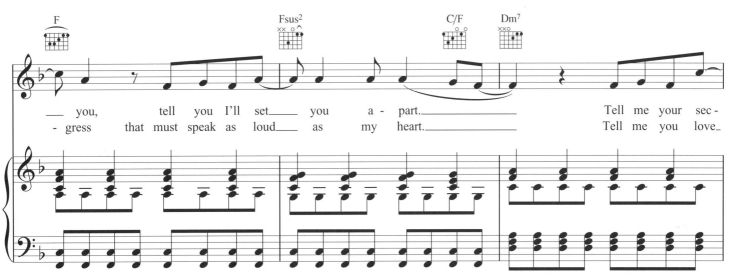

____ you, tell you I'll set____ you a - part. Tell me your sec -

-gress that must speak as loud____ as my heart._____ Tell me you love__

-rets and ask me your ques - tions, oh, let's go back to the start._____ Run - ning in cir -

____ me, come back and haunt__ me, oh and I rush to the start._____ Run - ning in cir -

Oh, take me back to the start.

(I'm go - ing)

SILENT SIGH

WORDS & MUSIC BY DAMON GOUGH

Ooh   aah   ooh   aah   ooh   aah   ooh   aah

ooh._____

Come   see what we   all   talk   a-bout,

peo - ple___ mov - ing to___ the moon. Stop, ba - by don't go, stop here.

Ne - ver stop liv - ing here___ till it eats the heart from_ your soul,

keeps down the sound_ of your si - lent___ sigh,_

si - lent sigh. Si - lent sigh,_ si - lent, si - lent, si - lent,

move_ me down,___ but don't_ love each o - ther.

SING FOR ABSOLUTION

WORDS & MUSIC BY MATTHEW BELLAMY, CHRIS WOLSTENHOLME & DOMINIC HOWARD

1.Lips are turn-ing blue, a kiss that can't re-new, I

(2.)no where left to hide, in no one to con-fide, the

be sing-ing___ and fall - ing from your___ grace.___

Ooh.___

2.There's

Oh._____

Sing for ab- so- lu- - -

won't be ex - - humed.

SON OF SAM

WORDS & MUSIC BY ELLIOTT SMITH

Medium tempo

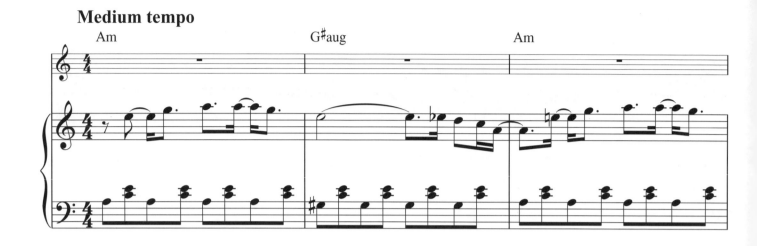

Some - thing's hap - pen - ing,___ don't___

STILL FIGHTING IT

WORDS & MUSIC BY BEN FOLDS

Good morn-ing son___ I am___ a bird___ wear-ing___ a brown___ po-ly-es-ter shirt.___ You want___ a Coke?___ May-be___ some fries?___ The roast___ beef com-bo's on-ly nine___ nine-ty five.___ (But) It's o-kay.___

STOP CRYING YOUR HEART OUT

WORDS & MUSIC BY NOEL GALLAGHER

Verse 2:
Get up, come on
Why you scared?
(I'm not scared)
You'll never change what's been and gone.

Cos all of the stars *etc.*

TALIHINA SKY
WORDS & MUSIC BY CALEB FOLLOWILL, NATHAN FOLLOWILL & ANGELO PETRAGLIA

Weeds blow tall on a bro-ken___ train track,

Bm7

trou - ble.   The knocked   up

D6

Bm7

girls   well they've all   got   their_____ share.

D6

Bm7

D.S. al Coda

Ruth seems out of mind, swears she won't give in this time._____

Coda

D6

Bm7

Life   goes   by_____   on a Ta - li - hi - na_____

113

WASH IN THE RAIN

WORDS & MUSIC BY PAUL BUTLER & AARON FLETCHER

1.Try and I fail, some-times_ I ev-en suc-ceed_ if you

3.Try - ing hard__

to for-get__ all the ef - fort we re-gret.__ But it__ won't

You would-n't stop.___

You would-n't stop.__

THIS LOVE

WORDS & MUSIC BY ADAM LEVINE, JAMES VALENTINE, JESSE CARMICHAEL, MICKEY MADDEN & RYAN DUSICK

1. I was__ so high__ I did__ not re-cog-nise__ the fire__ burn-ing

2. I tried__ my best__ to feed__ her ap-pe-tite,__ to keep her com-ing

123456789